Queen Anneena had a

1

Fifteen queens came to the feast.

Queen Jean had heaps of meat.

Queen Nelly had heaps of jelly.

But Queen Teeny Weeny did
not eat.

"Have some peas and beans," said Queen Jean.

"No," said Queen Teeny Weeny.

"Have some jelly and cream," said Queen Nelly.

"No," said Queen Teeny Weeny.

"What do you want to eat then?" said Queen Anneena.

"One green leaf," said Queen Teeny Weeny. But there was not a leaf to be seen!

Queen Anneena sent King Kareem
to the shop.

He came back with one green leaf.

Queen Anneena was happy to see Queen Teeny Weeny eat the leaf. "Do you want some tea and a sweet?" she said.

"No," said Queen Teeny Weeny.

"I am going home to clean my teeth."